A BOOK OF ACCOMPLISHMENTS

Scribble Scribe Press

HOW TO USE THIS BOOK

This isn't a to-do list notebook. This is a "that's done!" notebook.

Sometimes it's easy to forget all that we have accomplished for the day. Our to-do lists never seem to end and we might not feel like we have achieved all that we set out to do.

This journal is to help you keep track of all of those things you *did* accomplish, big and small.

DAY: Su M T W Th F (S)   DATE: *07 / 10 / 21*

NAILED IT!

[X] *Scheduled doctor's appointment*

[X] *Took out the trash*

[X] *Worked out for an hour*

[X] *Read 2 chapters in my book*

[X]

HOW I FEEL ABOUT THE DAY: ☹ 😐 ☺

I AM GRATEFUL FOR: *The beautiful weather we had today*

This Book Belongs to:

NAME: _____

PHONE: _____

EMAIL: _____

DAY: Su M T W Th F S   DATE:____/___/____

NAILED IT!

☒ ....

☒ ....

☒ ....

☒ ....

☒ ....

☒ ....

☒ ....

☒ ....

☒ ....

☒ ....

HOW I FEEL ABOUT THE DAY: ☹ 😐 ☺

I AM GRATEFUL FOR: ....

....

....

DAY: Su M T W Th F S   DATE:____ / ____ / ____

NAILED IT!

☒ ....

☒ ....

☒ ....

☒ ....

☒ ....

☒ ....

☒ ....

☒ ....

☒ ....

☒ ....

HOW I FEEL ABOUT THE DAY: ☹ 😐 ☺

I AM GRATEFUL FOR: ....
....
....

DAY: Su M T W Th F S   DATE:____/____/____

NAILED IT!

☒ ....

☒ ....

☒ ....

☒ ....

☒ ....

☒ ....

☒ ....

☒ ....

☒ ....

☒ ....

HOW I FEEL ABOUT THE DAY: ☹ 😐 ☺

I AM GRATEFUL FOR: ....
....
....

DAY: Su M T W Th F S   DATE:____/____/____

NAILED IT!

☒ ....

☒ ....

☒ ....

☒ ....

☒ ....

☒ ....

☒ ....

☒ ....

☒ ....

☒ ....

HOW I FEEL ABOUT THE DAY: ☹ 😐 ☺

I AM GRATEFUL FOR: ....
....
....

DAY: Su M T W Th F S   DATE:___/___/___

NAILED IT!

☒ ....

☒ ....

☒ ....

☒ ....

☒ ....

☒ ....

☒ ....

☒ ....

☒ ....

☒ ....

HOW I FEEL ABOUT THE DAY: ☹ 😐 ☺

I AM GRATEFUL FOR: ....
....
....

DAY: Su M T W Th F S   DATE: ___ / ___ / ___

NAILED IT!

- [x] ....
- [x] ....
- [x] ....
- [x] ....
- [x] ....
- [x] ....
- [x] ....
- [x] ....
- [x] ....
- [x] ....

HOW I FEEL ABOUT THE DAY: ☹ 😐 ☺

I AM GRATEFUL FOR: ....
....
....

DAY: Su M T W Th F S   DATE:____/____/____

NAILED IT!

☒ ....

☒ ....

☒ ....

☒ ....

☒ ....

☒ ....

☒ ....

☒ ....

☒ ....

☒ ....

HOW I FEEL ABOUT THE DAY: ☹ 😐 ☺

I AM GRATEFUL FOR: ....
....
....

DAY: Su M T W Th F S   DATE:____ / ___ / ____

NAILED IT!

☒ ....

☒ ....

☒ ....

☒ ....

☒ ....

☒ ....

☒ ....

☒ ....

☒ ....

☒ ....

HOW I FEEL ABOUT THE DAY: ☹ 😐 🙂

I AM GRATEFUL FOR: ....
....
....

DAY: Su M T W Th F S   DATE:___/___/___

NAILED IT!

☒ ....

☒ ....

☒ ....

☒ ....

☒ ....

☒ ....

☒ ....

☒ ....

☒ ....

☒ ....

HOW I FEEL ABOUT THE DAY: ☹ 😐 🙂

I AM GRATEFUL FOR: ....
....
....

DAY: Su M T W Th F S   DATE:____/___/____

NAILED IT!

☒ ....

☒ ....

☒ ....

☒ ....

☒ ....

☒ ....

☒ ....

☒ ....

☒ ....

☒ ....

HOW I FEEL ABOUT THE DAY: ☹ 😐 🙂

I AM GRATEFUL FOR: ....
....
....

DAY: Su M T W Th F S   DATE: ___ / ___ / ___

NAILED IT!

☒ ....

☒ ....

☒ ....

☒ ....

☒ ....

☒ ....

☒ ....

☒ ....

☒ ....

☒ ....

HOW I FEEL ABOUT THE DAY: ☹ 😐 🙂

I AM GRATEFUL FOR: ....

....

....

DAY: Su M T W Th F S   DATE:____/____/____

NAILED IT!

☒ ....

☒ ....

☒ ....

☒ ....

☒ ....

☒ ....

☒ ....

☒ ....

☒ ....

☒ ....

HOW I FEEL ABOUT THE DAY: ☹ 😐 🙂

I AM GRATEFUL FOR: ....

....

....

DAY: Su M T W Th F S   DATE:____/___/____

NAILED IT!

☒ ....

☒ ....

☒ ....

☒ ....

☒ ....

☒ ....

☒ ....

☒ ....

☒ ....

☒ ....

HOW I FEEL ABOUT THE DAY: ☹ 😐 ☺

I AM GRATEFUL FOR: ....
....
....

DAY: Su M T W Th F S   DATE: ___/___/___

NAILED IT!

☒ ....

☒ ....

☒ ....

☒ ....

☒ ....

☒ ....

☒ ....

☒ ....

☒ ....

☒ ....

HOW I FEEL ABOUT THE DAY: ☹ 😐 ☺

I AM GRATEFUL FOR: ....
....
....

DAY: Su M T W Th F S   DATE:_____/_____/_____

NAILED IT!

☒ ....

☒ ....

☒ ....

☒ ....

☒ ....

☒ ....

☒ ....

☒ ....

☒ ....

☒ ....

HOW I FEEL ABOUT THE DAY: ☹ 😐 ☺

I AM GRATEFUL FOR: ....
....
....

DAY: Su M T W Th F S   DATE:____/___/____

NAILED IT!

☒ ....

☒ ....

☒ ....

☒ ....

☒ ....

☒ ....

☒ ....

☒ ....

☒ ....

☒ ....

HOW I FEEL ABOUT THE DAY: ☹ 😐 🙂

I AM GRATEFUL FOR: ....
....
....

DAY: Su M T W Th F S   DATE:_____/___/_____

NAILED IT!

☒ ....

☒ ....

☒ ....

☒ ....

☒ ....

☒ ....

☒ ....

☒ ....

☒ ....

☒ ....

HOW I FEEL ABOUT THE DAY: ☹ 😐 ☺

I AM GRATEFUL FOR: ....

....

....

DAY: Su M T W Th F S   DATE:____/____/____

NAILED IT!

☒ ....

☒ ....

☒ ....

☒ ....

☒ ....

☒ ....

☒ ....

☒ ....

☒ ....

☒ ....

HOW I FEEL ABOUT THE DAY: ☹ 😐 ☺

I AM GRATEFUL FOR: ....

....

....

DAY: Su M T W Th F S   DATE:___/___/___

NAILED IT!

☒ ....

☒ ....

☒ ....

☒ ....

☒ ....

☒ ....

☒ ....

☒ ....

☒ ....

☒ ....

HOW I FEEL ABOUT THE DAY: ☹ 😐 ☺

I AM GRATEFUL FOR: ....

....

....

DAY: Su M T W Th F S   DATE:____/___/____

NAILED IT!

☒ ....

☒ ....

☒ ....

☒ ....

☒ ....

☒ ....

☒ ....

☒ ....

☒ ....

☒ ....

HOW I FEEL ABOUT THE DAY: ☹ 😐 ☺

I AM GRATEFUL FOR: ....
....
....

DAY: Su M T W Th F S   DATE:_____ / ___ / _____

NAILED IT!

☒ ....

☒ ....

☒ ....

☒ ....

☒ ....

☒ ....

☒ ....

☒ ....

☒ ....

☒ ....

HOW I FEEL ABOUT THE DAY: ☹ 😐 🙂

I AM GRATEFUL FOR: ....

....

....

DAY: Su M T W Th F S   DATE: ___/___/___

NAILED IT!

☒ ....

☒ ....

☒ ....

☒ ....

☒ ....

☒ ....

☒ ....

☒ ....

☒ ....

☒ ....

HOW I FEEL ABOUT THE DAY: ☹ 😐 ☺

I AM GRATEFUL FOR: ....

....

....

DAY: Su M T W Th F S   DATE: ___/___/___

NAILED IT!

☒ ....

☒ ....

☒ ....

☒ ....

☒ ....

☒ ....

☒ ....

☒ ....

☒ ....

☒ ....

HOW I FEEL ABOUT THE DAY: ☹ 😐 ☺

I AM GRATEFUL FOR: ....

....

....

DAY: Su M T W Th F S   DATE: ___ / ___ / ___

NAILED IT!

☒ ....

☒ ....

☒ ....

☒ ....

☒ ....

☒ ....

☒ ....

☒ ....

☒ ....

☒ ....

HOW I FEEL ABOUT THE DAY: ☹ 😐 ☺

I AM GRATEFUL FOR: ....

....

....

DAY: Su M T W Th F S   DATE:____/___/_____

NAILED IT!

☒ ....

☒ ....

☒ ....

☒ ....

☒ ....

☒ ....

☒ ....

☒ ....

☒ ....

☒ ....

HOW I FEEL ABOUT THE DAY: ☹ 😐 ☺

I AM GRATEFUL FOR: ....

....

....

DAY: Su M T W Th F S　　　DATE:___/___/___

NAILED IT!

☒ ....

☒ ....

☒ ....

☒ ....

☒ ....

☒ ....

☒ ....

☒ ....

☒ ....

☒ ....

HOW I FEEL ABOUT THE DAY: ☹ 😐 🙂

I AM GRATEFUL FOR: ....
....
....

DAY: Su M T W Th F S   DATE: ___ / ___ / ___

NAILED IT!

☒ ....

☒ ....

☒ ....

☒ ....

☒ ....

☒ ....

☒ ....

☒ ....

☒ ....

☒ ....

HOW I FEEL ABOUT THE DAY: ☹ 😐 ☺

I AM GRATEFUL FOR: ....

....

....

DAY: Su M T W Th F S   DATE:____/___/____

NAILED IT!

☒ ....

☒ ....

☒ ....

☒ ....

☒ ....

☒ ....

☒ ....

☒ ....

☒ ....

☒ ....

HOW I FEEL ABOUT THE DAY: ☹ 😐 ☺

I AM GRATEFUL FOR: ....
....
....

DAY: Su M T W Th F S   DATE:____/____/____

NAILED IT!

☒ ....

☒ ....

☒ ....

☒ ....

☒ ....

☒ ....

☒ ....

☒ ....

☒ ....

☒ ....

HOW I FEEL ABOUT THE DAY: ☹ 😐 ☺

I AM GRATEFUL FOR: ....
....
....

DAY: Su M T W Th F S   DATE:_____/_____/_____

NAILED IT!

☒ ....

☒ ....

☒ ....

☒ ....

☒ ....

☒ ....

☒ ....

☒ ....

☒ ....

☒ ....

HOW I FEEL ABOUT THE DAY: ☹ 😐 ☺

I AM GRATEFUL FOR: ....
....
....

DAY: Su M T W Th F S   DATE: ___ / ___ / ___

NAILED IT!

☒ ....

☒ ....

☒ ....

☒ ....

☒ ....

☒ ....

☒ ....

☒ ....

☒ ....

☒ ....

HOW I FEEL ABOUT THE DAY: ☹ 😐 ☺

I AM GRATEFUL FOR: ....
....
....

DAY: Su M T W Th F S   DATE:___/___/___

NAILED IT!

☒ ....

☒ ....

☒ ....

☒ ....

☒ ....

☒ ....

☒ ....

☒ ....

☒ ....

☒ ....

HOW I FEEL ABOUT THE DAY: ☹ 😐 ☺

I AM GRATEFUL FOR: ....

....

....

DAY: Su M T W Th F S   DATE:____/___/____

NAILED IT!

☒ ....

☒ ....

☒ ....

☒ ....

☒ ....

☒ ....

☒ ....

☒ ....

☒ ....

☒ ....

HOW I FEEL ABOUT THE DAY: ☹ 😐 ☺

I AM GRATEFUL FOR: ....

....

....

DAY: Su M T W Th F S   DATE:____/___/____

NAILED IT!

☒ ....

☒ ....

☒ ....

☒ ....

☒ ....

☒ ....

☒ ....

☒ ....

☒ ....

☒ ....

HOW I FEEL ABOUT THE DAY: ☹ 😐 ☺

I AM GRATEFUL FOR: ....
....
....

DAY: Su M T W Th F S   DATE:____/____/____

NAILED IT!

☒ ....

☒ ....

☒ ....

☒ ....

☒ ....

☒ ....

☒ ....

☒ ....

☒ ....

☒ ....

HOW I FEEL ABOUT THE DAY: ☹ 😐 ☺

I AM GRATEFUL FOR: ....
....
....

DAY: Su M T W Th F S   DATE:____ / ____ / ____

NAILED IT!

☒ ....

☒ ....

☒ ....

☒ ....

☒ ....

☒ ....

☒ ....

☒ ....

☒ ....

☒ ....

HOW I FEEL ABOUT THE DAY: ☹ 😐 ☺

I AM GRATEFUL FOR: ....
....
....

DAY: Su M T W Th F S   DATE:____/____/____

NAILED IT!

☒ ....

☒ ....

☒ ....

☒ ....

☒ ....

☒ ....

☒ ....

☒ ....

☒ ....

☒ ....

HOW I FEEL ABOUT THE DAY: ☹ 😐 🙂

I AM GRATEFUL FOR: ....

....

....

DAY: Su M T W Th F S   DATE:____ / ___ / _____

NAILED IT!

- [x] ....
- [x] ....
- [x] ....
- [x] ....
- [x] ....
- [x] ....
- [x] ....
- [x] ....
- [x] ....
- [x] ....

HOW I FEEL ABOUT THE DAY: 🙁 😐 🙂

I AM GRATEFUL FOR: ....
....
....

DAY: Su M T W Th F S   DATE: ___/___/___

NAILED IT!

☒ ....

☒ ....

☒ ....

☒ ....

☒ ....

☒ ....

☒ ....

☒ ....

☒ ....

☒ ....

HOW I FEEL ABOUT THE DAY: ☹ 😐 ☺

I AM GRATEFUL FOR: ....
....
....

DAY: Su M T W Th F S   DATE:____/____/____

NAILED IT!

☒ ....

☒ ....

☒ ....

☒ ....

☒ ....

☒ ....

☒ ....

☒ ....

☒ ....

☒ ....

HOW I FEEL ABOUT THE DAY: ☹ 😐 ☺

I AM GRATEFUL FOR: ....

....

....

DAY: Su M T W Th F S   DATE:___/___/___

NAILED IT!

☒ ....

☒ ....

☒ ....

☒ ....

☒ ....

☒ ....

☒ ....

☒ ....

☒ ....

☒ ....

HOW I FEEL ABOUT THE DAY: ☹ 😐 ☺

I AM GRATEFUL FOR: ....
....
....

DAY: Su M T W Th F S   DATE:____ / ___ / ____

NAILED IT!

☒ ....

☒ ....

☒ ....

☒ ....

☒ ....

☒ ....

☒ ....

☒ ....

☒ ....

☒ ....

HOW I FEEL ABOUT THE DAY: ☹ 😐 ☺

I AM GRATEFUL FOR: ....

....

....

DAY: Su M T W Th F S   DATE:___/___/___

NAILED IT!

☒ ....

☒ ....

☒ ....

☒ ....

☒ ....

☒ ....

☒ ....

☒ ....

☒ ....

☒ ....

HOW I FEEL ABOUT THE DAY: ☹ 😐 ☺

I AM GRATEFUL FOR: ....
....
....

DAY: Su M T W Th F S   DATE:___/___/___

NAILED IT!

☒ ....

☒ ....

☒ ....

☒ ....

☒ ....

☒ ....

☒ ....

☒ ....

☒ ....

☒ ....

HOW I FEEL ABOUT THE DAY: ☹ 😐 ☺

I AM GRATEFUL FOR: ....

....

....

DAY: Su M T W Th F S   DATE:_____ / ___ / _____

NAILED IT!

☒ ....

☒ ....

☒ ....

☒ ....

☒ ....

☒ ....

☒ ....

☒ ....

☒ ....

☒ ....

HOW I FEEL ABOUT THE DAY: ☹ 😐 ☺

I AM GRATEFUL FOR: ....

....

....

DAY: Su M T W Th F S   DATE:___/___/___

NAILED IT!

☒ ....

☒ ....

☒ ....

☒ ....

☒ ....

☒ ....

☒ ....

☒ ....

☒ ....

☒ ....

HOW I FEEL ABOUT THE DAY: ☹ 😐 ☺

I AM GRATEFUL FOR: ....

....

....

DAY: Su M T W Th F S   DATE: ___/___/___

NAILED IT!

☒ ....

☒ ....

☒ ....

☒ ....

☒ ....

☒ ....

☒ ....

☒ ....

☒ ....

☒ ....

HOW I FEEL ABOUT THE DAY: ☹ 😐 ☺

I AM GRATEFUL FOR: ....
....
....

DAY: Su M T W Th F S   DATE:____/___/____

NAILED IT!

☒ ....

☒ ....

☒ ....

☒ ....

☒ ....

☒ ....

☒ ....

☒ ....

☒ ....

☒ ....

HOW I FEEL ABOUT THE DAY: ☹ 😐 ☺

I AM GRATEFUL FOR: ....
....
....

DAY: Su M T W Th F S   DATE:____/___/_____

NAILED IT!

☒ ....

☒ ....

☒ ....

☒ ....

☒ ....

☒ ....

☒ ....

☒ ....

☒ ....

☒ ....

HOW I FEEL ABOUT THE DAY: ☹ 😐 ☺

I AM GRATEFUL FOR: ....

....

....

DAY: Su M T W Th F S   DATE:____ / ___ / ____

NAILED IT!

☒ ....

☒ ....

☒ ....

☒ ....

☒ ....

☒ ....

☒ ....

☒ ....

☒ ....

☒ ....

HOW I FEEL ABOUT THE DAY: ☹ 😐 ☺

I AM GRATEFUL FOR: ....
....
....

DAY: Su M T W Th F S   DATE:____/___/___

NAILED IT!

☒ ....

☒ ....

☒ ....

☒ ....

☒ ....

☒ ....

☒ ....

☒ ....

☒ ....

☒ ....

HOW I FEEL ABOUT THE DAY: ☹ 😐 ☺

I AM GRATEFUL FOR: ....

....

....

DAY: Su M T W Th F S   DATE:____/____/____

NAILED IT!

☒ ....

☒ ....

☒ ....

☒ ....

☒ ....

☒ ....

☒ ....

☒ ....

☒ ....

☒ ....

HOW I FEEL ABOUT THE DAY: ☹ 😐 ☺

I AM GRATEFUL FOR: ....
....
....

DAY: Su M T W Th F S   DATE:___ / ___ / ___

NAILED IT!

☒ ....

☒ ....

☒ ....

☒ ....

☒ ....

☒ ....

☒ ....

☒ ....

☒ ....

☒ ....

HOW I FEEL ABOUT THE DAY: ☹ 😐 ☺

I AM GRATEFUL FOR: ....
....
....

DAY: Su M T W Th F S   DATE:_____/_____/_____

NAILED IT!

☒ ....

☒ ....

☒ ....

☒ ....

☒ ....

☒ ....

☒ ....

☒ ....

☒ ....

☒ ....

HOW I FEEL ABOUT THE DAY: ☹ 😐 🙂

I AM GRATEFUL FOR: ....
....
....

DAY: Su M T W Th F S   DATE:___/___/___

NAILED IT!

☒ ....

☒ ....

☒ ....

☒ ....

☒ ....

☒ ....

☒ ....

☒ ....

☒ ....

☒ ....

HOW I FEEL ABOUT THE DAY: ☹ 😐 🙂

I AM GRATEFUL FOR: ....

....

....

DAY: Su M T W Th F S   DATE:___/___/___

NAILED IT!

☒ ....

☒ ....

☒ ....

☒ ....

☒ ....

☒ ....

☒ ....

☒ ....

☒ ....

☒ ....

HOW I FEEL ABOUT THE DAY: ☹ 😐 ☺

I AM GRATEFUL FOR: ....
....
....

DAY: Su M T W Th F S   DATE: ___ / ___ / ___

NAILED IT!

☒ ....

☒ ....

☒ ....

☒ ....

☒ ....

☒ ....

☒ ....

☒ ....

☒ ....

☒ ....

HOW I FEEL ABOUT THE DAY: ☹ 😐 ☺

I AM GRATEFUL FOR: ....

....

....

DAY: Su M T W Th F S   DATE: ___ / ___ / ___

NAILED IT!

[X] ....

[X] ....

[X] ....

[X] ....

[X] ....

[X] ....

[X] ....

[X] ....

[X] ....

[X] ....

HOW I FEEL ABOUT THE DAY: 🙁 😐 🙂

I AM GRATEFUL FOR: ....
....
....

DAY: Su M T W Th F S   DATE:____/____/____

NAILED IT!

☒ ....

☒ ....

☒ ....

☒ ....

☒ ....

☒ ....

☒ ....

☒ ....

☒ ....

☒ ....

HOW I FEEL ABOUT THE DAY: ☹ 😐 🙂

I AM GRATEFUL FOR: ....
....
....

DAY: Su M T W Th F S   DATE: ___ / ___ / ___

NAILED IT!

- ☒ ....
- ☒ ....
- ☒ ....
- ☒ ....
- ☒ ....
- ☒ ....
- ☒ ....
- ☒ ....
- ☒ ....
- ☒ ....

HOW I FEEL ABOUT THE DAY: ☹ 😐 ☺

I AM GRATEFUL FOR: ....
....
....

DAY: Su M T W Th F S   DATE:____/___/____

NAILED IT!

☒ ....

☒ ....

☒ ....

☒ ....

☒ ....

☒ ....

☒ ....

☒ ....

☒ ....

☒ ....

HOW I FEEL ABOUT THE DAY: ☹ 😐 ☺

I AM GRATEFUL FOR: ....

....

....

DAY: Su M T W Th F S   DATE:___ / ___ / ___

NAILED IT!

☒ ....

☒ ....

☒ ....

☒ ....

☒ ....

☒ ....

☒ ....

☒ ....

☒ ....

☒ ....

HOW I FEEL ABOUT THE DAY: ☹ 😐 ☺

I AM GRATEFUL FOR: ....
....
....

DAY: Su M T W Th F S   DATE:____/____/____

NAILED IT!

☒ ....

☒ ....

☒ ....

☒ ....

☒ ....

☒ ....

☒ ....

☒ ....

☒ ....

☒ ....

HOW I FEEL ABOUT THE DAY: ☹ 😐 ☺

I AM GRATEFUL FOR: ....
....
....

DAY: Su M T W Th F S   DATE:___/___/___

NAILED IT!

☒ ....

☒ ....

☒ ....

☒ ....

☒ ....

☒ ....

☒ ....

☒ ....

☒ ....

☒ ....

HOW I FEEL ABOUT THE DAY: ☹ 😐 ☺

I AM GRATEFUL FOR: ....
....
....

DAY: Su M T W Th F S   DATE:____ / ___ / ____

NAILED IT!

☒ ....

☒ ....

☒ ....

☒ ....

☒ ....

☒ ....

☒ ....

☒ ....

☒ ....

☒ ....

HOW I FEEL ABOUT THE DAY: ☹ 😐 🙂

I AM GRATEFUL FOR: ....
....
....

DAY: Su M T W Th F S   DATE:_____/____/_____

NAILED IT!

[X] ....

[X] ....

[X] ....

[X] ....

[X] ....

[X] ....

[X] ....

[X] ....

[X] ....

[X] ....

HOW I FEEL ABOUT THE DAY: ☹ 😐 ☺

I AM GRATEFUL FOR: ....

....

....

DAY: Su M T W Th F S   DATE:___/___/___

NAILED IT!

☒ ....

☒ ....

☒ ....

☒ ....

☒ ....

☒ ....

☒ ....

☒ ....

☒ ....

☒ ....

HOW I FEEL ABOUT THE DAY: ☹ 😐 ☺

I AM GRATEFUL FOR: ....
....
....

DAY: Su M T W Th F S   DATE:___/___/___

NAILED IT!

☒ ....

☒ ....

☒ ....

☒ ....

☒ ....

☒ ....

☒ ....

☒ ....

☒ ....

☒ ....

HOW I FEEL ABOUT THE DAY: ☹ 😐 ☺

I AM GRATEFUL FOR: ....

....

....

DAY: Su M T W Th F S   DATE: ___ / ___ / ___

NAILED IT!

☒ ....

☒ ....

☒ ....

☒ ....

☒ ....

☒ ....

☒ ....

☒ ....

☒ ....

☒ ....

HOW I FEEL ABOUT THE DAY: ☹ 😐 ☺

I AM GRATEFUL FOR: ....
....
....

DAY: Su M T W Th F S   DATE:____/____/____

NAILED IT!

☒ ....

☒ ....

☒ ....

☒ ....

☒ ....

☒ ....

☒ ....

☒ ....

☒ ....

☒ ....

HOW I FEEL ABOUT THE DAY: ☹ 😐 ☺

I AM GRATEFUL FOR: ....
....
....

DAY: Su M T W Th F S   DATE: ___ / ___ / ___

NAILED IT!

☒ ....

☒ ....

☒ ....

☒ ....

☒ ....

☒ ....

☒ ....

☒ ....

☒ ....

☒ ....

HOW I FEEL ABOUT THE DAY: ☹ 😐 ☺

I AM GRATEFUL FOR: ....

....

....

DAY: Su M T W Th F S   DATE:____ / ____ / ____

NAILED IT!

☒ ....

☒ ....

☒ ....

☒ ....

☒ ....

☒ ....

☒ ....

☒ ....

☒ ....

☒ ....

HOW I FEEL ABOUT THE DAY: ☹ 😐 ☺

I AM GRATEFUL FOR: ....

....

....

DAY: Su M T W Th F S   DATE:____/____/____

NAILED IT!

☒ ....

☒ ....

☒ ....

☒ ....

☒ ....

☒ ....

☒ ....

☒ ....

☒ ....

☒ ....

HOW I FEEL ABOUT THE DAY: ☹ 😐 ☺

I AM GRATEFUL FOR: ....

....

....

DAY: Su M T W Th F S   DATE:___/___/___

NAILED IT!

☒ ....

☒ ....

☒ ....

☒ ....

☒ ....

☒ ....

☒ ....

☒ ....

☒ ....

☒ ....

HOW I FEEL ABOUT THE DAY: ☹ 😐 ☺

I AM GRATEFUL FOR: ....
....
....

DAY: Su M T W Th F S   DATE:___/___/___

NAILED IT!

☒ ....

☒ ....

☒ ....

☒ ....

☒ ....

☒ ....

☒ ....

☒ ....

☒ ....

☒ ....

HOW I FEEL ABOUT THE DAY: ☹ 😐 ☺

I AM GRATEFUL FOR: ....
....
....

DAY: Su M T W Th F S   DATE:____/____/____

NAILED IT!

☒ ....

☒ ....

☒ ....

☒ ....

☒ ....

☒ ....

☒ ....

☒ ....

☒ ....

☒ ....

HOW I FEEL ABOUT THE DAY: ☹ 😐 🙂

I AM GRATEFUL FOR: ....

....

....

DAY: Su M T W Th F S   DATE:____/____/____

NAILED IT!

☒ ....

☒ ....

☒ ....

☒ ....

☒ ....

☒ ....

☒ ....

☒ ....

☒ ....

☒ ....

HOW I FEEL ABOUT THE DAY: ☹ 😐 ☺

I AM GRATEFUL FOR: ....

....

....

DAY: Su M T W Th F S   DATE: ___/___/___

NAILED IT!

☒ ....

☒ ....

☒ ....

☒ ....

☒ ....

☒ ....

☒ ....

☒ ....

☒ ....

☒ ....

HOW I FEEL ABOUT THE DAY: ☹ 😐 ☺

I AM GRATEFUL FOR: ....

....

....

DAY: Su M T W Th F S   DATE:___/___/___

NAILED IT!

☒ ....

☒ ....

☒ ....

☒ ....

☒ ....

☒ ....

☒ ....

☒ ....

☒ ....

☒ ....

HOW I FEEL ABOUT THE DAY: ☹ 😐 ☺

I AM GRATEFUL FOR: ....

....

....

DAY: Su M T W Th F S   DATE:___/___/___

NAILED IT!

☒ ....

☒ ....

☒ ....

☒ ....

☒ ....

☒ ....

☒ ....

☒ ....

☒ ....

☒ ....

HOW I FEEL ABOUT THE DAY: ☹ 😐 ☺

I AM GRATEFUL FOR: ....

....

....

DAY: Su M T W Th F S   DATE:____/____/____

NAILED IT!

☒ ....

☒ ....

☒ ....

☒ ....

☒ ....

☒ ....

☒ ....

☒ ....

☒ ....

☒ ....

HOW I FEEL ABOUT THE DAY: ☹ 😐 🙂

I AM GRATEFUL FOR: ....
....
....

DAY: Su M T W Th F S   DATE:___/___/___

NAILED IT!

- [x] ....
- [x] ....
- [x] ....
- [x] ....
- [x] ....
- [x] ....
- [x] ....
- [x] ....
- [x] ....
- [x] ....

HOW I FEEL ABOUT THE DAY: ☹ 😐 ☺

I AM GRATEFUL FOR: ....
....
....

DAY: Su M T W Th F S   DATE:____/____/____

NAILED IT!

☒ ....

☒ ....

☒ ....

☒ ....

☒ ....

☒ ....

☒ ....

☒ ....

☒ ....

☒ ....

HOW I FEEL ABOUT THE DAY: ☹ 😐 🙂

I AM GRATEFUL FOR: ....
....
....

DAY: Su M T W Th F S   DATE:___/___/___

NAILED IT!

- [x] ....
- [x] ....
- [x] ....
- [x] ....
- [x] ....
- [x] ....
- [x] ....
- [x] ....
- [x] ....
- [x] ....

HOW I FEEL ABOUT THE DAY: ☹ 😐 ☺

I AM GRATEFUL FOR: ....
....
....

DAY: Su M T W Th F S   DATE:____/____/____

NAILED IT!

☒ ....

☒ ....

☒ ....

☒ ....

☒ ....

☒ ....

☒ ....

☒ ....

☒ ....

☒ ....

HOW I FEEL ABOUT THE DAY: ☹ 😐 ☺

I AM GRATEFUL FOR: ....

....

....

DAY: Su M T W Th F S   DATE:___ / ___ / ___

NAILED IT!

☒ ....

☒ ....

☒ ....

☒ ....

☒ ....

☒ ....

☒ ....

☒ ....

☒ ....

☒ ....

HOW I FEEL ABOUT THE DAY: ☹ 😐 ☺

I AM GRATEFUL FOR: ....

....

....

DAY: Su M T W Th F S   DATE:_____/___/_____

NAILED IT!

☒ ....

☒ ....

☒ ....

☒ ....

☒ ....

☒ ....

☒ ....

☒ ....

☒ ....

☒ ....

HOW I FEEL ABOUT THE DAY: ☹ 😐 ☺

I AM GRATEFUL FOR: ....
....
....

DAY: Su M T W Th F S   DATE:____ / ___ /____

NAILED IT!

☒ ....

☒ ....

☒ ....

☒ ....

☒ ....

☒ ....

☒ ....

☒ ....

☒ ....

☒ ....

HOW I FEEL ABOUT THE DAY: ☹ 😐 ☺

I AM GRATEFUL FOR: ....

....

....

DAY: Su M T W Th F S   DATE:____ / ___ / ____

NAILED IT!

☒ ....

☒ ....

☒ ....

☒ ....

☒ ....

☒ ....

☒ ....

☒ ....

☒ ....

☒ ....

HOW I FEEL ABOUT THE DAY: ☹ 😐 🙂

I AM GRATEFUL FOR: ....

....

....

DAY: Su M T W Th F S   DATE: ___/___/___

NAILED IT!

☒ ....

☒ ....

☒ ....

☒ ....

☒ ....

☒ ....

☒ ....

☒ ....

☒ ....

☒ ....

HOW I FEEL ABOUT THE DAY: ☹ 😐 🙂

I AM GRATEFUL FOR: ....
....
....

DAY: Su M T W Th F S   DATE:___/ /___

NAILED IT!

- ☒ ....
- ☒ ....
- ☒ ....
- ☒ ....
- ☒ ....
- ☒ ....
- ☒ ....
- ☒ ....
- ☒ ....
- ☒ ....

HOW I FEEL ABOUT THE DAY: ☹ 😐 ☺

I AM GRATEFUL FOR: ....
....
....

DAY: Su M T W Th F S   DATE:___ / ___/ ___

NAILED IT!

☒ ....

☒ ....

☒ ....

☒ ....

☒ ....

☒ ....

☒ ....

☒ ....

☒ ....

☒ ....

HOW I FEEL ABOUT THE DAY: ☹ 😐 ☺

I AM GRATEFUL FOR: ....
....
....

DAY: Su M T W Th F S   DATE:____/____/____

NAILED IT!

☒ ....

☒ ....

☒ ....

☒ ....

☒ ....

☒ ....

☒ ....

☒ ....

☒ ....

☒ ....

HOW I FEEL ABOUT THE DAY: ☹ 😐 ☺

I AM GRATEFUL FOR: ....

....

....

DAY: Su M T W Th F S   DATE:___/___/___

NAILED IT!

- [x] ....
- [x] ....
- [x] ....
- [x] ....
- [x] ....
- [x] ....
- [x] ....
- [x] ....
- [x] ....
- [x] ....

HOW I FEEL ABOUT THE DAY: ☹ 😐 ☺

I AM GRATEFUL FOR: ....
....
....

DAY: Su M T W Th F S   DATE:_____/____/_____

NAILED IT!

☒ ....

☒ ....

☒ ....

☒ ....

☒ ....

☒ ....

☒ ....

☒ ....

☒ ....

☒ ....

HOW I FEEL ABOUT THE DAY: ☹ 😐 ☺

I AM GRATEFUL FOR: ....
....
....

DAY: Su M T W Th F S   DATE:____/___/____

NAILED IT!

☒ ....

☒ ....

☒ ....

☒ ....

☒ ....

☒ ....

☒ ....

☒ ....

☒ ....

☒ ....

HOW I FEEL ABOUT THE DAY: ☹ 😐 🙂

I AM GRATEFUL FOR: ....
....
....

DAY: Su M T W Th F S   DATE:_____/___/_____

NAILED IT!

☒ ....

☒ ....

☒ ....

☒ ....

☒ ....

☒ ....

☒ ....

☒ ....

☒ ....

☒ ....

HOW I FEEL ABOUT THE DAY: ☹ 😐 🙂

I AM GRATEFUL FOR: ....

....

....

DAY: Su M T W Th F S   DATE:____/___/____

NAILED IT!

☒ ....

☒ ....

☒ ....

☒ ....

☒ ....

☒ ....

☒ ....

☒ ....

☒ ....

☒ ....

HOW I FEEL ABOUT THE DAY: ☹ 😐 ☺

I AM GRATEFUL FOR: ....

....

....

DAY: Su M T W Th F S   DATE:____/___/____

NAILED IT!

☒ ....

☒ ....

☒ ....

☒ ....

☒ ....

☒ ....

☒ ....

☒ ....

☒ ....

☒ ....

HOW I FEEL ABOUT THE DAY: ☹ 😐 🙂

I AM GRATEFUL FOR: ....

....

....

DAY: Su M T W Th F S   DATE:___ / ___ / ___

NAILED IT!

☒ ....

☒ ....

☒ ....

☒ ....

☒ ....

☒ ....

☒ ....

☒ ....

☒ ....

☒ ....

HOW I FEEL ABOUT THE DAY: ☹ 😐 ☺

I AM GRATEFUL FOR: ....
....
....

Made in the USA
Monee, IL
29 June 2022

98830753R00059